JOHN
GALSWOR

JOHN GALSWORTHY

The Forsyte Saga

The Man of Property
In Chancery
To Let

A Modern Comedy

The White Monkey
The Silver Spoon
Swan Song

Heinemann/Octopus

The Man of Property first published in Great Britain in 1906
In Chancery first published in Great Britain in 1920
To Let first published in Great Britain in 1921
The White Monkey first published in Great Britain in 1924
The Silver Spoon first published in Great Britain in 1926
Swan Song first published in Great Britain in 1928

This edition first published in 1976 by
William Heinemann Limited
15–16 Queen Street, London W1
in association with
Octopus Books Limited
59 Grosvenor Street, London W1

ISBN 0 7064 0572 2

Printed in Great Britain by
Jarrold & Sons Ltd, Norwich

Contents

Introduction

JOHN GALSWORTHY is the most thoroughly English novelist since Dickens. The background, characters and situations which he creates in his work comprise a literary edifice as solid, imposing and specifically English as Lloyd's, the Stock Exchange and the Bank of England. But his novels are by no means inanimate masses of verbal masonry which sit immovable on their foundations as mere triumphs of a writer's architectural and engineering ability. To take the simile further one might say that the noble and imposing façades are illuminated by the artist's creative *son et lumière*, the tragedy, comedy and irony of life observed and transmuted into the highlights and shadows of fiction.

John Galsworthy was born in 1867 and came from Devonshire landed gentry stock. He was educated at Harrow and New College, Oxford where he took an honours degree in law in 1889. He was called to the bar by Lincoln's Inn but preferred to travel and sailed in merchant ships to the Far East, meeting at one point that other literary voyager, Joseph Conrad. His first book was a collection of stories entitled *From the Four Winds* (1897) which he wrote under the name 'John Sinjohn', a pseudonym retained for three further books, two novels and a second collection of stories. A novel, *The Island Pharisees* (1904), was the first to appear under his own name and in 1906 came *The Man of Property*, the first of that great series 'The Forsyte Saga' and 'A Modern Comedy'.

The two greatest literary influences on Galsworthy were not, as it happens, English writers, but Russian and French. In his youth he read and re-read the works of Turgenev and Maupassant and although his own books are as firmly part of the society and ways of his own country as the carved mahogany furniture, the dark-green velvet upholstery, and the saddle of mutton traditionally set on Forsyte dinner tables, his view of the dying society which he describes is as affectionate and sensible of its charm as it is ironic.

The Forsyte Saga, continued in *A Modern Comedy* (1929), charts the course of successive generations and the tenacity of the possessive instinct–so evident in Soames Forsyte–through the half-century that included the great War, the birth and rise of socialism and the appearance of those cracks in the social structure that became so inevitably and visibly irreparable fissures. Galsworthy himself said of *The Forsyte Saga* that 'it cannot be absolved from the charge of embalming the upper middle-class life'. But it is that triumph of preservation that allows readers today to enter a vanished way of life and to experience and be captivated by it again and again on both the printed page and so outstandingly on the television screen.

Galsworthy was a skilled and successful dramatist and it was in recognition of both novels and plays that in 1929 he was awarded the order of merit and in 1932, the year of his death, the Nobel Prize for Literature. But his most enduring memorial is his work of which he said: 'If the upper middle class, with other classes, is destined to "move on" into amorphism, here, pickled in these pages, it lies under glass for strollers in the wide and ill-arranged museum of Letters to gaze at. Here it rests, preserved in its own juice: The Sense of Property.'

FORSYTE FAMILY TREE

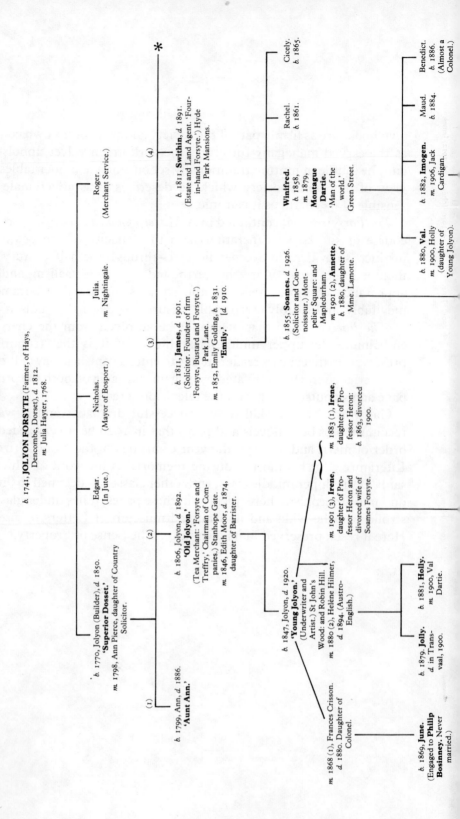

b 1741, **JOLYON FORSYTE** (Farmer, of Hays,
Dencombe, Dorset), d 1812.
m. Julia Hayter, 1768.

*

(1)

Edgar.
(In Jute.)

Nicholas.
(Mayor of Bosport.)

Julia.
m. Nightingale.

Roger.
(Merchant Service.)

(4)

b 1811, **Swithin**, d 1891.
(Estate and Land Agent. 'Four-
in-hand Forsyte.') Hyde
Park Mansions.

b 1799, Ann, d 1886.
'**Aunt Ann**.'

(2)

b 1770, Jolyon (Builder), d 1850.
'**Superior Dosset**.'
m. 1798, Ann Pierce, daughter of Country
Solicitor.

b 1806, Jolyon, d 1892.
'**Old Jolyon**,'
(Tea Merchant: 'Forsyte and
Treffry,' Chairman of Com-
panies.) Stanhope Gate.
m. 1846, Edith Moor, d 1874,
daughter of Barrister.

(3)

b 1811, **James**, d 1901.
(Solicitor. Founder of firm
'Forsyte, Bustard and Forsyte.')
Park Lane.
m. 1852, Emily Golding, b 1831.
'**Emily**,'   [d 1910.

b 1855, **Soames**. d 1926.
(Solicitor and Con-
noisseur.) Mont-
pelier Square: and
Mapledurham.
m. 1901 (2), **Annette**,
b 1880, daughter of
Mme. Lamotte.

b 1858, **Winifred**.
m. 1879,
**Montague
Dartie**.
'Man of the
world.'
Green Street.

Rachel.
b 1861.

Cicely.
b 1865.

b 1847, Jolyon, d 1920.
'**Young Jolyon**.'
(Underwriter and
Artist.) St John's
Wood: and Robin Hill.

m. 1868 (1), Frances Crisson.
d 1880. Daughter of
Colonel.

m. 1880 (2), Heléne Hilmer,
d 1894. (Austro-
English.)

m. 1883 (1), **Irene**,
daughter of Pro-
fessor Heron.
b 1863, divorced
1900.

}

m. 1901 (3), **Irene**,
daughter of Professor Heron and
divorced wife of
Soames Forsyte.

b 1869, **June**.
(Engaged to **Philip
Bosinney**. Never
married.)

b 1879, **Jolly**.
d in Trans-
vaal, 1900.

b 1881, **Holly**.
m. 1900, Val
Dartie.

b 1880, **Val**.
m. 1900, Holly
(daughter of
Young Jolyon).

b 1882, **Imogen**.
m. 1906, Jack
Cardigan.

Maud.
b 1884.

Benedict.
b 1886.
(Almost a
Colonel.)

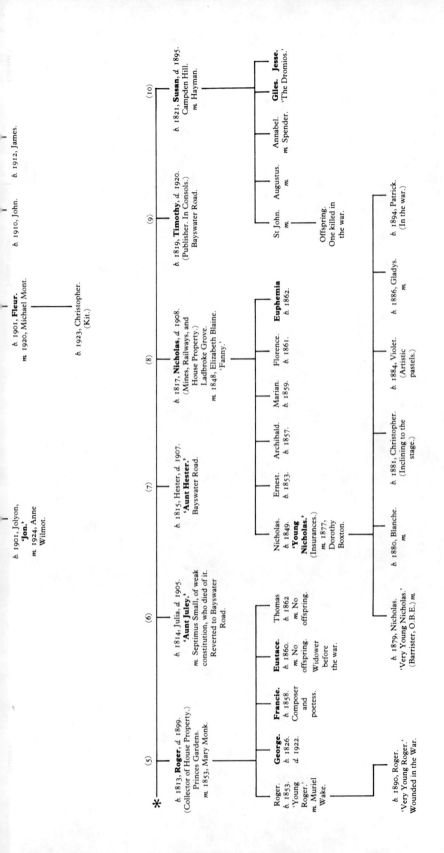

b. 1901, Jolyon, **'Jon.'** m. 1924, Anne Wilmot.

b. 1901, **Fleur.** m. 1920, Michael Mont.

b. 1910, John.

b. 1912, James.

b. 1923, Christopher. (Kit.)

*

(5) b. 1813, **Roger**, d. 1899. (Collector of House Property.) Princes Gardens. m. 1853, Mary Monk.

(6) b. 1814, Julia, d. 1905. 'Aunt Juley.' m. Septimus Small, of weak constitution, who died of it. Reverted to Bayswater Road.

(7) b. 1815, Hester, d. 1907. 'Aunt Hester.' Bayswater Road.

(8) b. 1817, **Nicholas**, d. 1908. (Mines, Railways, and House Property.) Ladbroke Grove. m. 1848, Elizabeth Blaine. 'Fanny.'

(9) b. 1819, **Timothy**, d. 1920. (Publisher. In Consols.) Bayswater Road.

(10) b. 1821, **Susan**, d. 1895. Campden Hill. m. Hayman.

St John. m.

Augustus. m.

Annabel. m. Spender.

Giles. Jesse. 'The Dromios.'

Offspring. One killed in the war.

Roger. b. 1853. 'Young Roger.' m. Muriel Wake.

George. b. 1826. d. 1922.

Francie. b. 1858. Composer and poetess.

Eustace. b. 1860. m. No offspring. Widower before the war.

Thomas. b. 1862. m. No offspring.

Nicholas. b. 1849. 'Young Nicholas.' (Insurances.) m. 1877, Dorothy Boxton.

Ernest. b. 1853.

Archibald. b. 1857.

Marian. b. 1859.

Florence. b. 1861.

Euphemia b. 1862.

b. 1890, Roger. 'Very Young Roger.' Wounded in the War.

b. 1879, Nicholas. 'Very Young Nicholas.' (Barrister, O.B.E.) m.

b. 1880, Blanche. m.

b. 1881, Christopher. (Inclining to the stage.)

b. 1884, Violet. (Artistic pastels.)

b. 1886, Gladys. m.

b. 1894, Patrick. (In the war.)

The Forsyte Saga

BOOK I

The Man of Property

THE FORSYTE SAGA
To my wife

I dedicate the Forsyte Saga
in its entirety,
believing it to be of all my work
the least unworthy of one
without whose encouragement, sympathy,
and criticism
I could never have become even
such a writer as I am

THE MAN OF PROPERTY

'. . . You will answer
The slaves are ours . . .'
Merchant of Venice

TO EDWARD GARNETT

PART I

I

'AT HOME' AT OLD JOLYON'S

Those privileged to be present at a family festival of the Forsytes have seen that charming and instructive sight—an upper middle-class family in full plumage. But whosoever of these favoured persons has possessed the gift of psychological analysis (a talent without monetary value and properly ignored by the Forsytes), has witnessed a spectacle, not only delightful in itself, but illustrative of an obscure human problem. In plainer words, he has gleaned from a gathering of this family—no branch of which had a liking for the other, between no three members of whom existed anything worthy of the name of sympathy—evidence of that mysterious concrete tenacity which renders a family so formidable a unit of society, so clear a reproduction of society in miniature. He has been admitted to a vision of the dim roads of social progress, has understood something of patriarchal life, of the swarmings of savage hordes, of the rise and fall of nations. He is like one who, having watched a tree grow from its planting—a paragon of tenacity, insulation, and success, amidst the deaths of a hundred other plants less fibrous, sappy, and persistent—one day will see it flourishing with bland, full foliage, in an almost repugnant prosperity, at the summit of its efflorescence.

On June 15, 1886, about four of the afternoon, the observer who chanced to be present at the house of old Jolyon Forsyte in Stanhope Gate, might have seen the highest efflorescence of the Forsytes.

This was the occasion of an 'At Home' to celebrate the engagement of Miss June Forsyte, old Jolyon's grand-daughter, to Mr Philip Bosinney. In the bravery of light gloves, buff waistcoats, feathers and frocks, the family were present—even Aunt Ann, who now but seldom left the corner of her brother Timothy's green drawing-room, where, under the ægis of a plume of dyed pampas grass in a light blue vase, she sat all day reading and knitting, surrounded by the effigies of three generations of Forsytes. Even Aunt Ann was there; her inflexible back and the dignity of her calm old face personifying the rigid possessiveness of the family idea.

When a Forsyte was engaged, married, or born, the Forsytes were present; when a Forsyte died—but no Forsyte had as yet died; they did not die; death being contrary to their principles, they took precautions against it, the instinctive precautions of highly vitalised persons who resent encroachments on their property.

About the Forsytes mingling that day with the crowd of other guests, there was a more than ordinary groomed look, an alert, inquisitive assurance, a brilliant respectability, as though they were attired in defiance of something. The habitual sniff on the face of Soames Forsyte had spread through their ranks; they were on their guard.

The subconscious offensiveness of their attitude has constituted old Jolyon's 'at home' the psychological moment of the family history, made it the prelude of their drama.

The Forsytes were resentful of something, not individually, but as a family; this resentment expressed itself in an added perfection of raiment, an exuberance of family cordiality, an exaggeration of family importance, and–the sniff. Danger–so indispensable in bringing out the fundamental quality of any society, group, or individual–was what the Forsytes scented; the premonition of danger put a burnish on their armour. For the first time, as a family, they appeared to have an instinct of being in contact with some strange and unsafe thing.

Over against the piano a man of bulk and stature was wearing two waistcoats on his wide chest, two waistcoats and a ruby pin instead of the single satin waistcoat and diamond pin of more usual occasions, and his shaven, square, old face, the colour of pale leather, with pale eyes, had its most dignified look, above his satin stock. This was Swithin Forsyte. Close to the window, where he could get more than his fair share of fresh air, the other twin, James–the fat and the lean of it, old Jolyon called these brothers–like the bulky Swithin, over six feet in height, but very lean, as though destined from his birth to strike a balance and maintain an average, brooded over the scene with his permanent stoop; his grey eyes had an air of fixed absorption in some secret worry, broken at intervals by a rapid, shifting scrutiny of surrounding facts; his cheeks, thinned by two parallel folds, and a long, clean-shaven upper lip, were framed within Dundreary whiskers. In his hands he turned and turned a piece of china. Not far off, listening to a lady in brown, his only son Soames, pale and well-shaved, dark-haired, rather bald, had poked his chin up sideways, carrying his nose with that aforesaid appearance of 'sniff', as though despising an egg which he knew he could not digest. Behind him his cousin, the tall George, son of the fifth Forsyte, Roger, had a Quilpish look on his fleshy face, pondering one of his sardonic jests.

Something inherent to the occasion had affected them all.

Seated in a row close to one another were three ladies–Aunts Ann, Hester (the two Forsyte maids), and Juley (short for Julia), who not in first youth had so far forgotten herself as to marry Septimus Small, a man of poor constitution. She had survived him for many years. With her elder and younger sister she lived now in the house of Timothy, her sixth and youngest brother, on the Bayswater Road. Each of these ladies held fans in their hands, and each with some touch of colour, some emphatic feather or brooch, testified to the solemnity of the opportunity.

In the centre of the room, under the chandelier, as became a host, stood the head of the family, old Jolyon himself. Eighty years of age, with his fine, white hair, his dome-like forehead, his little, dark grey eyes, and an immense white moustache, which drooped and spread below the level of his strong jaw, he had a patriarchal look, and in spite of lean cheeks and hollows at his temples, seemed master of perennial youth. He held himself extremely upright, and his shrewd, steady eyes had lost none of their clear shining. Thus he gave an impression of superiority to the doubts and dislikes of smaller men. Having had his own way for innumerable years, he had earned a prescriptive right to it. It